The Origins of the Garratt Locomotive

R. L. Hills, M.A., Ph.D., D.I.C.

Preface

This small book is based on the booklet "The Garratt Patent Locomotive" originally published by Beyer, Peacock & Co. Ltd of Gorton, Manchester in 1911 and reprinted with additional material about 1921. The original was kindly lent by Dr. Richard L. Hills who also contributed the introductory notes and provided the various illustrations and original artwork used in this reprint.

Dr. Hills is the author of "Beyer, Peacock – Locomotive Builders to the World", the full history of Beyer, Peacock & Co. Ltd. and presented a paper to the Newcomen Society on "The Origins of the Garratt Locomotive" to a joint meeting of The Newcomen Society and the Institution of Mechanical Engineers in London on 21st, May 1980.

All royalties from the sale of this book are being donated by the author towards the cost of restoring "K1", the very first Beyer Garratt Locomotive.

Andrew Neale

© (New Material) – Dr. R. L. Hills & Plateway Press, May 2000

First published 2000

ISBN 1 871980 43 7

PLATEWAY PRESS

Taverner House, Harling Road, East Harling, Norfolk NR16 2QR

Printed in England by POSTPRINT
Taverner House, Harling Road, East Harling, Norfolk NR16 2QR

FRONT COVER ILLUSTRATION:
The World's first Garratt Locomotive, K1, is seen under test at Beyer Peacock's works at Gorton, Manchester before shipment to Tasmania in 1909. *(H. W. Garratt Archive)*

BACK COVER ILLUSTRATION:
Pioneer Garratt K1 seen at Dinas Junction shops in June 1995 before work began to render her suitable for service on the re-opened Welsh Highland Railway. *(R. L. Hills)*

FRONTISPIECE:
The pioneer Garratt Locomotive, K1, poses for the photographer in the Tasmanian forests served by the North East Dundes Tramway, probably soon after entering service there in 1909. *(H. W. Garratt Archive)*

The Origins of the Garratt Locomotive

PART 1

Early Training and Career

Herbert William Garratt was born on 6th June 1864, in London and died, aged 49, on 25th September 1913, at Richmond, Surrey. I met his daughter, the late Mrs Mumford, while I was Director of the Northern Western Museum of Science and Industry in Manchester. After being educated at various private schools in London, Garratt formed his first definite association with railways by serving an apprenticeship from 1879 to 1882 in the Locomotive Works of the North London Railway at Bow. He passed through the various branches and showed his ability as a draughtsman. He possessed considerable ability also as an artist and Mrs Mumford presented some of his paintings to the Museum. These included one of a Great Western broad gauge 4-2-2 emerging from below a road bridge with suitable smoke effects and another, the Great Eastern No. 603 heading into the sunrise (or perhaps sunset?). The *Graphic* published one of his paintings in November 1897 "showing the horrors of the live cattle and sheep trade", and the comment was made by the Director of the Central Argentine Railway that Garratt might "have a brilliant career before you as an artist".

For a time, he changed his allegiance to steam ships and, from Bow, moved to William Doxford's Marine Engine Works at Sunderland, for employment as an ordinary fitter. In 1883, he went to sea as Fourth and Third Engineer respectively on the steamships *Umtata* and *Congella* belonging to Bullard, King & Co.'s Direct Natal Line of steamers. At the beginning of 1884, he made the trip from Gravesend to New York as Third Engineer on board the U.S. Arctic Relief ship, *Alert,* before it left for the Arctic.

From his paintings and other interests, it is suspected that his first love was railways and he returned to then when, in 1885, he became inspecting engineer for Douglas Fox at Glasgow where some goods engines were built by Neilson's for the Central Argentine Railway. What he was doing at Abergavenny until the middle of 1886 is unknown but after that he was working for the London and South Western Railway in connection with the Vacuum Brake Company until early in 1889. This was followed by his first tour overseas, with the Central Argentine Railway, where he remained until August 1897. It will be noted that Garratt had a series of short-term contracts, a pattern that continued for the rest of his life. This has not been compared with other railway engineers at that time so we do not know how typical it was. Mrs Mumford was quite an imperious lady who was reputed to have many of her father's characteristics. Some photos show him flashily dressed so it is quite probable that he managed to upset his superiors, which may account for his frequent changes of jobs.

Very early in his life, Garratt showed his capacity for invention. In November 1885, he took out patent 13,937 for "An Improvement in the Expansion of the Valve Gear of Locomotive and other Steam Engines". This was an idea for lengthening the slots in radius links of reversing gears to allow, by an extra movement of the reversing lever, the slide valve to be moved by hand to open the port when an engine had stopped at a dead centre. His later patents covered an improved boiled egg opener in 1901 as well as, of course, the famous "Garratt" locomotive in 1907.

His time in the Argentine may have been the happiest part of his life. In April 1889, he was appointed temporary head draughtsman on the Central Argentine Railway, while the holder of that office was on leave. He was sent back to England that October to make arrangements for fitting the locomotives and stock of this railway with vacuum brakes and was put in charge of this work on his return. Then he supervised the installation of Pintsch's system of gas lighting in the carriages and workshops which also included the erection of three gasworks. During November and December 1893, he was in charge of the Rosario Works while there was a fitters' strike and he carried arms to protect the railway company's property.

In March 1894, Garratt was appointed District Locomotive Superintendent at Pergamino, a 300 mile district. Among his duties, he had to clear up the mess after an accident as well as driving the dining and sleeping car trains during the drivers' strike in 1896. Later that year, he was able to keep his fitters at work repairing his engines while others were on strike elsewhere. He ought to have been granted leave every three years, but, such was the pressure of work, that he was not able to return to England until February 1897 after he had been unwell and in hospital for a time. He was asked to inspect some engines being built in Britain and had his leave extended so he could visit "various works in the North". Garratt decided to seize the opportunity of returning in a boat on which his younger brother was engineer but unfortunately this delayed him and he arrived back late. The new General Manager dismissed him, even though he recognised that Garratt had done a good job. The officers and men of the railway presented him with a gold watch, chain and a testimonial with 130 signatures.

The reasons for dismissing a man who appears to have done a good job will never be discovered now, but this was a pattern that would be repeated in following years. We have seen how Garratt had obtained experience in a broad range of different aspects of the railway industry, covering particularly design, construction, maintenance and operation of railway locomotives. The next years would broaden this so his dismissal from the Central Argentine Railway may have contributed toward the evolution of the Garratt locomotive.

After he returned to England, in 1899 he submitted a provisional application for another patent but no final specification followed. This was to keep sand in the boxes on locomotives dry by building the boxes partly inside the smokebox. When filling them in this position, sand would not be poured all over the valve motion. This idea was brought to the attention of Messrs. Dubs & Co., but there is doubt whether it was taken up. However, it shows Garratt's concern for improving the performance of locomotives, not by major innovations, but by attention to small details, which would assist those responsible for operating the machines. Another idea at this period, which does not seem to have reached the patent stage, was for a spark extinguisher. He fitted this to engine No. 13 on the Pergamino-San Nicholas run where it operated effectively. There was also a point lock and indicator coupled to the distant signal which showed in which direction the points were set and whether they were locked.

Garratt's next appointment was in 1900 as Locomotive Superintendent on the Cuban Central Railways. He reorganised the workshops and was very popular with the men. But the General Manager ordered him to place a young person straight from his

1) H. W. Garratt and some of his staff pose proudly by the Lagos Government Rly. Locomotive erected in record time in 1902.

(H. W. Garratt Archive)

apprenticeship in England as Second Foreman in the Concha Shops and demote the Spaniard already holding the post. Garratt protested and decided it was best to accept a financial settlement and resign. The person in question was unable to do any good in Cuba and returned to England, only to be dismissed a second time after he proved to be useless on the Algeciras Railway as well. Once again, Garratt received many letters and other expressions of regret that he was leaving Cuba from the people among whom we had worked.

Garratt followed this with a one year appointment on the Lagos Government Railway where he found the locomotive department in a shambolic state when he took charge in February 1902. Only three engines could turn their wheels; no spare parts had been ordered from England, and it was feared that the railway might have to stop altogether. Yet, by dint of extraordinary exertions, Garratt pulled things together so that, within seven weeks by the middle of April, he was able to inform the Traffic Superintendent that the full train service could be resumed. One, a 2-6-0 tender locomotive, was finished in the record time of 32 working hours from commencing to uncrate it until it was in steam. The whole job was done by four European fitters and fourteen natives and was claimed to be the quickest piece of such work in West Africa. Such labour needed the fullest co-operation of the staff under him and photographs have survived showing Garratt and some of his fitters standing proudly by this locomotive. He wrote a report on the reorganisation of the Locomotive Department to show how running expenses might be reduced. It is possible that this might have upset some of the senior staff, because it seems that his administration ability was doubted and this, with once again a period of ill-health for the climate did not suit him, were the official reasons why the Crown Agents would not renew his appointment, although he had worked on for an extra three months.

From Lagos, he returned to London, but was soon abroad again, this time in 1904 to the Lima Railways in Peru as Resident Engineer and Locomotive Superintendent. Once again, he was involved with running a railway during a strike and received a letter of thanks from the Management for the "pluck shown in your endeavours to keep up the traffic". As in both Cuba and Lagos, Garratt reorganised the locomotive department and was able to effect a saving of £10,000 per annum in wages in the shops at Calloa. Unfortunately, due to a take-over bid and future probable electrification, Garratt was declared redundant and given a first-class passage home to England in April 1905. A comment in one of Mrs Mumford's letters suggest that he met her mother in Peru and returned with her.

The Garratt Patent

It was during this next period of enforced idleness that Garratt conceived his patent locomotive. Mrs Mumford said in 1973 that one of her aunts, then aged 95, remembered how her father returned from Peru in 1905 and, because he had no other job and it was a difficult time for him, was working all out on his new invention. Mrs Mumford herself was not born until 1907 so knew nothing about this period but saved some of his papers and books of cuttings which show some of the origins of his ideas. Later when he was living at Richmond but probably also earlier in his life, Garratt had his own workshop where Mrs Mumford said he used to spend much of his time. She was only rarely allowed into this "wonder" as a child of five. It may have been soon after his return from Peru that Garratt constructed a $2^3/_4$ inch gauge model 4-4-0 tender engine from proprietary parts, worked by live steam at about 40 p.s.i. through a paraffin blow-lamp burner mounted in the tender. In many ways, it is typical of his patent locomotive, a series of well-proved principles combined into a successful engine.

His new form of locomotive was obviously based on his experience of operating locomotives under difficult conditions, especially abroad, where the track might be light and poorly laid; where curves might be severe and bridges weak; where gradients could be steep and locomotives underpowered. His preliminary sketches are undated and the earliest date we now have for his invention is that of the application for the patent, 26th July 1907, but the basic idea must have been conceived much earlier. His address was then 25 Leweston Place, Portland Avenue, Stamford Hill, Middlesex, his mother's house.

The Origins of the Garratt Locomotive
PART 2

Rival Articulated Designs

The articulated locomotive presented the possibility of combining two driving units under one boiler. Not only could this be operated by one engine crew but the length of the wheelbase of each coupled unit could be reasonably short. This made traversing sharp curves easier while the weight could be distributed over a longer distance with more axles, enabling a heavier locomotive to traverse light track. Disadvantages were the extra complexity of the steam and exhaust pipe connections and the method of articulation.

Garratt's scrap book has cuttings of examples of the semi-articulated type, the Mallet. Anatole Mallet originally devised this type as a system of compounding in France in 1884. It evolved into a boiler mounted on a frame carrying one set of non-articulated driving wheels with, in front of them, another set on a pivoted frame. The front set was always at this time the low pressure unit of a compound, which avoided high pressure steam pipe connections. Garratt's illustrations include the Mallets supplied by Borsig for the Central Northern Railway of the Argentine in 1904 and the 0-6 + 6-0 Mallet for the Central Railway of Brazil built by the American Locomotive Company in 1908 as well as some for North China. Originally the Mallet was a tank locomotive, but, by 1904, the fuel and water supplies were carried in a tender. While this enabled the diameter of the boiler barrel to be increased, the firebox was still restricted, either in width by being placed between the driving wheels, or in depth when placed above them to avoid increasing the height of the centre of gravity and of the whole engine. In addition, the boiler barrels generally extended over the front set of driving wheels, making the tubes longer than necessary for maximum efficiency. Through the non-articulated wheels being placed well towards the rear, the front end of the boiler swung out a long way when the locomotive was passing round curves. While the Mallet had become very popular by 1904, it was generally still only a slow moving goods engine with usually only driving wheels and no carrying or guiding wheels.

There were two true articulated types, the Meyer and the Fairlie. Robert Fairlie patented his locomotive in 1864. Its concept was derived from two locomotives joined at their firebox. The boiler was a continuous unit with a chimney at either end. In the middle was a pair of fireboxes which exhausted in different directions through their respective tubes and chimneys. Below each boiler barrel was placed a power bogie with the cylinders at the outer ends. While the fireboxes could be deep because they were situated between the two engine units, their width was restricted by the need to fire them from the side as well as the water tanks and fuel bunkers which had to be placed on either side of the boiler and carried on this framing. By 1905, a few designs were appearing with outer guiding wheels to give greater stability to the engine units. The illustration Garratt had of a Fairlie was one built by the Saxon Engine Works in 1902 for the Saxon State Railway. This was a tramway version with the motion enclosed and the cylinders at the inner ends of the bogies. There was a driving position at either end in front of the smokebox, a feature of which Garratt would have approved as it gave the driver a good view of the track ahead. However the whole engine seems top heavy and looks unstable.

The prototype for the system adopted by J. J. Meyer dated back to the double bogie 0-4 + 4-0 tank "Weiner Neustadt" entered in the Semmering trials of 1851. The first Meyer locomotive was the "L'Avenir", a standard gauge 0-4 + 4-0 built in 1867. The boiler, water tanks and fuel bunker were mounted on a rigid frame underneath which were the two engine units linked together. Boiler dimensions were restricted both by the water tanks alongside and the engine units underneath. Du Bousquet's Meyers of 1905 for the Northern Railway of France were among Garratt's cuttings.

Kitsons of Leeds improved the Meyer type in 1894 when three 3ft 6ins gauge 0-6 + 6-0 were purchased by the Angllo-Chilean Nitrate Railway. By separating the power units, the firebox could be dropped between them, which at least gave ample depth and easy access to the ashpan, although its width was still restricted by the water tanks at the sides. Up to 1907, Kitsons supplied five orders for the Kitson-Meyer type for various railways. From the point of view of the boiler, the Kitson-Meyer had the best design of all the semi- and full-articulated locomotives. It may have been this which caused Garratt to approach Kitsons over his locomotive because other cuttings show that it was boiler design which greatly influenced him.

While Garratt's concept of his locomotive arose out of his experience on various railways, he was never in charge of any other types of articulated engines but was aware of the short-comings of other designs. In 1909 a letter in the Garratt Archives, written probably by Beyer, Peacock to S. J. Sarjant of the Great Indian Peninsular Railway, stated,

> "You will observe that in detail there is no novelty, neither does the engine embrace any experimental and untried components. As a matter of fact, this design of locomotive embraces four leading features, the principles of which are old, and can be found in the "Fairlie" engine introduced forty years ago, and other similar types now being presented by Locomotive Builders, but these features, as combined by Garratt, have resulted in the development of a locomotive of such striking originality and usefulness, that it is a marvel to me how Fairlie – and others since who have been engaged in developing the articulated locomotive – could have missed such an obviously simple solution of reconciling a properly designed boiler of large capacity to the limits of the various loading gauges".

Garratt knew at first hand through his experiences at Lagos the difficulties of raising steam in the boilers then fitted to most narrow gauge engines with fireboxes restricted in width by the driving wheels. The 2-6-0 tender locomotives which he erected in Nigeria were 3ft 6ins gauge with inside frames. While the diameter of the Belpaire boiler appears quite sufficient, the firebox width was severely restricted by being placed between the frames. But, if the firebox was raised clear of the wheels, the grate became shallow and the centre of gravity dangerously high. He studied reports of the Salisbury accident of 1906 where the engine left the rails through taking the curve too fast. Aspinall of the Lancashire & Yorkshire railway liked a high centre of gravity because it gave a long period of rolling oscillation but conditions were different on the narrow gauge with a broader loading gauge in proportion to the rail gauge.

If the line of the boiler could be kept low, there would be an improved view from the footplate. Garratt knew how vital it was for the drivers to have a clear view of the road ahead, particularly on lines laid in remote areas where animals or other obstructions might have blocked the track. In his cuttings book, he had pictures of the North British Atlantic No. 868 and a Lancashire & Yorkshire 4 cylinder express engine, both with fireboxes which obscured the view from the driver's position. In contrast, there is a suggested arrangement for an express locomotive hauling a separate water tank coupled at the smokebox end so that the driver could have a good view from the spacious cab on the footplate. This engine ran in the opposite direction from normal and could have been derived from Planchar's Italian "Mucca", which was similarly arranged and details of which were published in England in 1903.

The Initial Concept of the Garratt Locomotive

Garratt's first very rough sketch shows that he had conceived an engine with a boiler mounted on its own frame with the possibility of a driving cab at either end. To the rear was one set of driving wheels with the fuel bunker and water tank mounted on it while the front set of wheels might be either under the boiler barrel or, as was the case in all later Garratt designs, in front of the boiler with a water tank as well. The cylinders were sketched in at the outer ends of the bogies. The firebox and ashpan reached almost to rail level. His ideas were further developed in a pair of drawings mounted on one sheet of paper. Here we find two 0-4-0 + 0-4-0 with large diameter driving wheels, powered by cylinders at the inner ends of the bogies. Such an arrangement might have kept the steam pipes shorter. The wheels were set well clear of the boiler, which could then be dropped low in its frame to give an unusually low centre of gravity. On one drawing, at each end of the boiler cradle, were placed driving cabs, so that the engineman would have a clear view of the road ahead. Garratt's engine was thus a perfect "double-ender", and could travel equally well in either direction.

The opening words of the provisional specification for his patent read,

> "The principal object being to admit of a combination of an extremely large boiler combined with any required size of wheels and a low centre of gravity".

By placing his engine units at either end of his boiler, Garratt realised that the diameter of the wheels could be increased so that his locomotive would be capable of reaching much higher speeds. Therefore from the beginning, he envisaged his engine as more than just a slow narrow gauge goods type.

Locating the water tanks and fuel bunker on the engine units gave the Garratt its great advantage and distinctive features over other articulated designs. Not only did this lessen the strains and forces on the pivots, but it enabled the boiler to be developed to almost the maximum permitted by the loading gauge. The Garratt single boiler and firebox was much cheaper to construct and maintain than the double one of the Fairlie and was restricted in width only by the carrying frame and steam pipes passing along the sides. The firebox could be dropped almost to rail level and was easily accessible for washing out and also cleaning the ashes out of the pan. The diameter of the boiler barrel could approach the limits of the loading gauge and it could remain low not only to keep the centre of gravity low but also to give a better view from the cab and with adequate height to the steam dome and chimney. Through the large diameter, a greater number of tubes could be fitted inside and, just as important, the barrel could be shorter. The evaporative power of boiler tubes decreased rapidly with their length and a number of short tubes was more efficient than fewer tubes of greater length giving the same heating surface. Also, with long tubes, an excessive draught was needed in the firebox which was obtained only by a corresponding increase in back-pressure in the cylinders.

The reduced length of the Garratt boiler had an additional advantage over both the Mallet and Fairlie on lines with steep gradients because the extreme variations in water level did not cause the top of the firebox or the ends of the tubes to become exposed. In South Africa, this was used to advantage with the Garratts which could travel anywhere on that system whereas the Mallets were limited. So Garratt must have realised that the boilers on his new locomotive would be safer as well as steaming more freely, which his experience on railways abroad had taught him was very necessary.

The pivots would be placed at either end of Garratt's boiler "cradle". He saw this as giving the engine greater stability because no part would overhang the outer rails when going round a curve. The cradle and boiler would form a chord across the arc of the curve and so the sharper the curve the more the boiler would move in towards the centre. Just how Garratt envisaged mounting this cradle on the engine units is difficult to follow in his provisional specification and his early idea of a frame made from four "I" bars would certainly have been more complex than later designs.

The Origins of the Garratt Locomotive
PART 3

The Position at Beyer, Peacock

It is surprising the Beyer, Peacock should have been interested in backing a new and completely untried design of articulated locomotive because this company had a reputation for building high-class, well-engineered locomotives. As the name of Rolls Royce would become renowned in the car industry, so Beyer, Peacock had established itself in the railway locomotive industry. Its products had achieved world-wide fame and its engines could be found on every continent. 1902 is a convenient date at which to commence our examination because in that year the private limited company was bought out and the firm became Beyer, Peacock & Co. (1902) Limited. Colonel Ralph Peacock, the son of one of the founders Richard, retired as Chairman and, although he remained as a Director until 1906, this really marked the end of the connections with the original founders. The new administration had to face changing conditions in the locomotive industry through increased competition from other builders, through railways electrifying and of course electric tramway systems, as well as through the application of the internal combustion engine to both rail but more particularly road transport.

At home, orders were still being obtained from some railways in Britain, but the policy of building locomotives in their own workshops continued to operate in contrast with the United States of America. In Scotland, three companies in Glasgow – Sharp Stewart, Neilson Reid and Dubs – amalgamated in 1903 to form the North British Locomotive Co., creating what was then the largest firm of locomotive builders in Europe. Similar expansion was taking place elsewhere. Germany emerged as a serious competitor in the overseas market. Japan, where Beyer, Peacock sold many locomotives, established its own locomotive building industry in 1908. The pace of railroad construction lessened in North America after 1900 and with it the demand for locomotives there so that the two great American builders, the American Locomotive Company and Baldwins, began to look elsewhere to sell their products. Production at Baldwins rose from 501 engines in 1897 to just under 2,700 in 1907. In the latter year after major expansion and reorganisation, Baldwins employed 18,500 men, placing it among the largest American industrial employers. Figures for Beyer, Peacock were 90 engines in 1897 which had risen to 147 in 1907. No figures are available for the number of men employed in 1907 but in 1928 it was a mere 2,395. This shows the formidable competition Beyer, Peacock faced.

When Gorton Foundry closed in 1966, a series of reports from this period was discovered, showing that the Directors were actively considering what other products might be manufactured to lessen dependence on a single product. Perhaps these papers were a lucky find and a chance survival from many similar ones because it is not known how often the Board investigated the company's trading position in this way. What these papers show is that the Directors were actively considering their options, among which would later be Garratt's proposal for his articulated locomotive.

The introduction of electric tramcars, from 1885 onwards, had resulted in a great expansion of tramway routes, taking some passengers from the railways. Some railways had responded by electrification, which of course reduced the demand for steam locomotives. Colonel Peacock feared that electric traction would speedily replace steam. P. A. Creeke was therefore asked in 1902 by the Beyer, Peacock Board to investigate what problems would have to be faced and what extra manufacturing capacity would be needed if Gorton Foundry were to enter the electric traction field. Because there was no National Grid at this period, any railway electrifying its lines had to purchase the generating equipment, the distribution system including transformers and either third rails or overhead wires, as well as the electric trains themselves. A decision would have to be to made to determine how much of all this equipment Beyer, Peacock could make a start and enter this expanding market by concentrating on constructing electric locomotives and rolling stock, in which field they already had expertise, and buying-in the electrical components. A few electric locomotives were built at Gorton in later years but the prophecy of doom for the steam locomotive itself was half a century too early.

The development of the internal combustion engine posed another threat to the steam railway locomotive. It started the revival of road transport, not only with the private car but also with road haulage and public service vehicles. In 1903, A. P. Jameson, Beyer, Peacock's representative in London, suggested that Beyer, Peacock should erect an experimental motor car which Harry Livesey had designed. In May of that year, R. R. Lister, Works Manager, was taken on a demonstration run through the crowded centre of London in an American Fischer thirty-seater omnibus. He also investigated the Rochet-Schneider motor car but it was realised that a different approach to production would be needed. Railway locomotives were generally built in small batches, but motor cars needed long production runs. This would not be possible with existing machine tools at Gorton Foundry. The works could not be easily altered for this type of assembly if the manufacture of railway locomotives were to continue as well. A few steam lorries were made at Gorton between 1904 and 1906 but no further road vehicles were ever attempted.

Of more significance may have been the visit to Serpollet's works in Paris also in 1903. This firm specialised in both motor cars and railcars with light-weight steam engines and flash-steam boilers. Further discussions with this company were held but the eight railcars that were built at Gorton all had conventional boilers, single driving axles and outside cylinders and valve gear. Once again, this venture proved to be short-lived and no more were built after 1905. The couple delivered to the London, Brighton & South Coast Railway which were used between Eastbourne and Hastings, were said to vibrate badly at any speed, but the North Staffordshire Railway must have been more satisfied with their first couple for another was ordered later.

Locomotive orders were poor in 1903 with 93 built but, in the following years, production began to increase, reaching a peak of 152 in 1908. This may be the reason why Beyer, Peacock's interest in pursuing alternative products waned but equally concentration on steam locomotive production avoided substantial capital investment in new plant and major rearranging of the works. For railways, one way of meeting road competition was to enlarge the capacity of trains. Costs would be reduced because only one locomotive and train crew would be needed. Therefore the size of railway locomotives increased rapidly during the opening years of the twentieth century. Beyer, Peacock tended to specialise in the larger, heavier locomotives. They met this challenge and increased their construction capacity by building a new boiler shop in the early 1920s. One answer to increasing locomotive power was the articulated locomotive. Beyer, Peacock's interest in Garratt's proposals could have been that, with such an engine of their own design, they could offer customers a full range of types and power.

Beyer, Peacock's supplied two pairs of back-to-back 2-6-0 + 0-6-2 locomotives for the Inter Oceanic Railway in 1889 but otherwise had built no articulated locomotives. The Design Office at Gorton had been aware for a long time of this demand because, in the 1809s, schemes were produced for one simple and three compound Fairlies, two of these being prepared for the Mogyana Railway where some of the first Garratts went. A "modified Fairlie", with two separate boilers, was proposed for the Burma Railways, later a major customer for Garratts. Early in the 20th century, three Mallet designs were prepared. Two of these, those for the Portuguese State Railway in 1904 and the Arica Railway, Chile, in 1906, were prepared by Samuel Jackson. The Tasmanian Government Railways received two slightly different schemes for a 2ft gauge Mallet prepared on 2nd and 5th April 1907. While these were being discussed in Tasmania, a 2ft gauge 0-4-0 + 0-4-0 Fairlie scheme was prepared for the New South Wales Government Railways. This engine is shown with only one firehole, a fault corrected forty years earlier! The date for this drawing is 29th July 1907, the same month as Garratt deposited his provisional specification.

The Development of the Garratt Locomotive

Kitsons were one British company with experience in building articulated locomotives so Garratt approached them about building his new locomotive. In Kitson's history[1], it is stated,

> "In 1907, Mr H. W. Garratt called Airdale Foundry to submit his patent for articulation. I have said elsewhere that in those early days there was not much reticence as to mechanical opinion. Kitsons expressed a decided lack of enthusiasm for another engineer's 'damned improvements' and the Garratt idea was not taken up by Kitsons".

If the drawings which Garratt showed to Kitsons were those of his early designs, it is hardly surprising that he was rejected. But Garratt's fortunes were about to change. On 7th August 1907, he obtained employment as an inspecting engineer in Britain for the New South Wales Government Railways. Contracts had been placed with Beyer, Peacock for three different designs of standard gauge locomotives, a 4-6-4 tank and a 4-6-0 and 2-8-0 tender types. These orders amounted to 55 locomotives which were delivered in 1907/8. We do not know when Garratt first visited Gorton to inspect these locomotives but it seems reasonable to suppose that the New South Wales Fairlie scheme was mentioned to him and it is just as likely that he discussed his provisional specification with the Design Staff because here was his great chance if his patent engine were ever to be built.

1 Kitsons of Leeds, 1837-1937, Edwin Kitson Clark, L. P. C.

At the beginning of October 1907, Garratt sent some blueprints and drawings to Gorton and Jackson who prepared the first Garratt scheme on the 9th of that month. This was a replacement for the Fairlie for New South Wales and the drawing shows an 0-4-0 + 0-4-0 with cylinders at the inner ends of the bogies. The cylinder and wheel dimensions were the same as those for the Fairlie. A year later, a larger 2ft 6ins gauge version was sent to the New South Wales Public Works department but no orders resulted. In the meantime during November 1907, Garratt moved to Manchester with his family and lived in Albert Road, Levenshulme.

Garratt must have had many discussions with the Drawing Office staff at Gorton because the Complete Specification, submitted on 24th January 1908 shows considerable design advances over his original suggestions. When his first drawings are compared with those printed in his patent, it is evident that the Garratt locomotive has been "Beyer Peacockified" and now looks like an engine that would work satisfactorily. Even Jackson's first scheme has much better proportions. Samuel Jackson was an outstanding locomotive engineer. He was apprenticed at Crewe Works before moving to Beyer, Peacock as a pupil in 1900. He worked in the design department and became Assistant Works Manager in 1913. From 1918 to 1924 he was Works Manager and then was appointed Advisory and Development Engineer. Mrs Mumford said that her parents were on friendly terms with the Jacksons and often visited each other. With Jackson's ability and later friendship with Garratt, it is probable that he was the person at Beyer, Peacock who saw the potential in this form of articulated locomotive and was willing to support its adoption by his Company.

There must have been further correspondence with Tasmania because, in April 1908, a slightly heavier version of the New South Wales first 2ft Garratt scheme was dispatched. This design again followed Garratt's early concept with the cylinders at the inner ends of the bogies. This scheme had the same wheel arrangement as the Mallet proposal, the same stroke, but the Garratt was to be a simple with all four cylinders 10 ins bore. This was not accepted by the people in Tasmania who must have wanted a compound. Accordingly, a modified scheme was sent in January 1909, still four coupled, but the rear bogie had two high pressure cylinders 11ins diameter and the front bogie had the low pressure ones, 17ins diameter. Both these dimensions were the same as those in the larger Mallet proposal. Using large cylinders on the front bogie meant that the boiler frame had to be cranked to clear them. Boiler pressures ranged from 180lb psi for the Mallet, 160lb psi for the simple and 195lb psi for the compound Garratt.

The designs show the great advantage of the Garratt principle. The firebox on the Mallet was long, narrow and shallow, for it had to be perched above the driving wheels. The Garratt firebox was short, broad and deep, with 10 sq ft greater heating surface and nearly 3 sq ft larger grate area. The Garratt boiler was shorter but the surface area of the tubes remained almost the same because their number was increased from 152 to 170 of the larger diameter. The Tasmanian authorities must have been pleased with this design because, on receipt of the second scheme, they responded almost immediately by enquiring about a couple of locomotives and placed a firm order for one on 28th January 1909. This was followed on 12th March for a second, and so commenced the construction of the K Class Garratts.

Agents:–Beyer, Peacock & Co. Locomotive Engineers, Gorton Foundry, Manchester

"GARRATT" LOCOMOTIVES

(Patented)

TO

YOUR

PLEASE

QUOTE

HERBERT W. GARRATT M.I.Mech.E.
Locomotive Engineer.

(Consulting & Inspecting)
Late Locomotive Supt.
L.G. Ry. C.C. Rys., L. Rys, &c.

20, Albert Road Levenshulme,

Manchester,

————————————19———

Dear Sir,
　　　　I beg to enclose a leaflet, descriptive of the new type
of high duty locomotive, that I am bringing out.
　　　　Some of the advantages offered by this improved engine
over existing types as follows:-
Very great steaming capacity.
Simplicity of construction.
Reduced deadweight for the power exerted.
Best shape of firebox for the proper consumption of fuel, with
large square grate, and great number of tubes.
Accessibility of all parts for repairs, lubrication, &c.
Great stability on curves.
Excellent distribution of weight.
Easy running, with good look-out.
Economical first cost.
I, or Messrs. Beyer, Peacock & Co. (my agents) will be glad to
supply information required, & to furnish estimates, designs,
&c. for engines to meet special conditions.
　　　　　　　　　Yours faithfully,

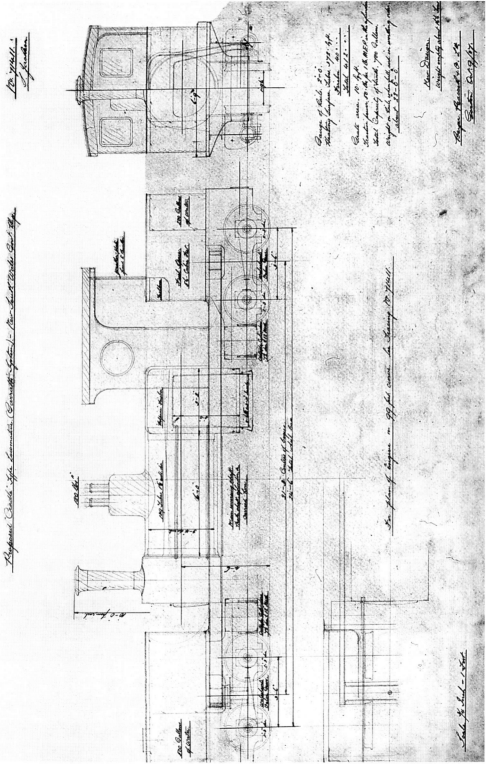

2) The drawing for the first proposed Garratt locomotive

(H. W. Garratt Archive)

The Complete Specification

In the meantime, Garratt's patent was accepted on 11th June 1908 (Patent 17,165) and, on 31st July it was proposed that Garratt enter into an agreement with Beyer, Peacock, which was settled on 18th September 1908, outlining the terms of royalties, licences, etc. This has not survived. However his position as inspecting engineer for the New South Wales Government Railways was terminated on 31st August 1908. A problem arose with the Consulting Engineer, Mr Davis, over some drawings and Garratt resigned to devote all his time to developing his engine.

Garratt's Complete Specification may reflect suggestions made by the design staff at Gorton. Also we can learn a lot by examining the first Garratt locomotive, that for the 2ft gauge Tasmanian Government Railways, K1, because this is a large engine and no "toy". Just how much of a pioneering design K1 was will be recognised when it is realised that not only had Beyer, Peacock never constructed an articulated locomotive but, with the exception of the 1ft 6ins gauge works shunters for themselves and Horwich, they had never built any engines for such a narrow gauge. There were the couple of 0-6-0 tank engines for the 2ft 6ins Welshpool & Llanfair Railway in 1902 which were said to have been based on the 0-4-2 2ft 4½ins Glyn Valley Tramway engines in 1888. In 1889, an 0-4-0 tram engine of 2ft 9ins gauge was supplied to A. L. Elder & Co. Then we come to the 3ft gauge Isle of Man locomotives and the like. So designing a 2ft gauge locomotive would have been quite a challenge for the staff at Gorton even without it being an entirely new type of locomotive.

The importance Garratt (and Beyer, Peacock too) attached to good boiler design is clear from the comparison on K1's dimensions with those of the Mallet already mentioned. What will also be noticed about K1 is how low this boiler could be set in the frames with tall cab and chimney, so the driver had a good view, while the firebox is broad and deep. Many overseas railways had to import their fuel and the best Welsh steam coal would have been expensive even if available. The managerial staff of such railways would have welcomed an engine that would burn anything and still produce a good head of steam.

Garratt's cradle of "I" bars in his provisional specification was replaced by a simplified plate frame, a feature which remained standard to the last. The swinging links fastening the cradle to the bogies were replaced by a cylindrical pivot, again a design which formed the basis of this vital part and the focus of much development through the years. The Complete Specification lays great emphasis on the fuel bunker and water tanks being placed on the engine units. These could be of large capacity and yet made low so as not to obscure the driver's view. There is a certain irony here when the final designs of Beyer-Garratt are examined because these tanks reach almost to the top of the loading gauge, while the enormous boilers almost completely obscure the view ahead from the cab.

The Complete Specification says that these water and coal tanks can be kept low and flat, "this greatly assisting to render the engine stable". This can well be understood when compared with the side tanks perched high up beside the boilers on other articulated locomotives where they could have contributed to a rolling motion. Garratt also made great claims for placing the tanks on the engine units,

3) and 4)   Two views of one of the pair of the very first Garratt locomotives – the Tasmanian "K" class – under construction at Beyer, Peacock's works in 1909.

"tending to keep the bogies steady as against the disturbing forces of the steam acting on the pistons, which in previous double bogie engines has caused the bogies to have a wriggling movement, especially at high speeds".

This may be doubted because ordinary engines may also "wriggle" along, but it is true that Garratts were capable of reaching high speeds. Those built for South Africa in the 1920s were reaching speeds of over 50 mph while the Mallets were unsafe at 30.

The major change between Garratt's original sketch and his early drawings with those submitted in the Complete Specification is the position of the pivot on the bogies. Garratt placed the pivot in the centre of the four-coupled wheels, where it was also placed in the Tasmanian K Class. But somebody took the crucial step in the illustration for the Complete Specification of moving the pivot towards the inner ends of the engine units. Although in this drawing the pivots are placed between the large driving wheels of a 2-4-0 + 0-4-2, they are no longer at the centre of the bogie and the weight must have been distributed across the wheels through compensating beams. The out-of-centre pivots are shown also on a 0-6-0 + 0-6-0 sketch of the same date. All subsequent Garratt designs, starting with the second for the Darjeeling Himalayan Railway 0-4-0 + 0-4-0 have pivots out of centre. Was this a Beyer, Peacock contribution, possibly Jackson's, which allowed Garratt to develop into the enormous designs of later years with wheel arrangements for example of 4-8-4 + 4-8-4?

The Complete Specification contains further points showing the advantages of the Garratt method of articulation. What is evident is that Garratt, almost certainly with the help of Beyer, Peacock, had evolved a design which was capable of having a boiler of ample dimensions and which would be free steaming; a design which had the potential of travelling at high speed with remarkable steadiness through the positioning of the fuel bunker and water tanks on the engine units; a design which gave the driver a much better view of the track ahead in whichever direction; and finally a design which was inherently a better system of articulation through the way in which the various units were linked together. The development of the Garratt locomotive by Beyer, Peacock over the next fifty years amply justified Garratt's original claims.

The
GARRATT
Patent
LOCOMOTIVE

THE FURTHER DEVELOPMENT
OF THE
STEAM LOCOMOTIVE

NOTES ON THE
"GARRATT" TYPE

Patented in all the Principal Countries of the World

BEYER, PEACOCK & CO. LTD.
LOCOMOTIVE ENGINEERS,
GORTON, MANCHESTER,
ENGLAND

MANCHESTER:
Taylor, Garnett, Evans & Co. (Hudson & Kearns, Ltd.)

A Description of a New Type
of Locomotive Engine, combining
Great Power with Simplicity of
Construction

THE practical limit of large locomotive *Demand for* design on hitherto recognised principles *Greater* of construction has been admittedly reached, *Power* but urgent need still exists for more power, and the necessity has arisen for a new type of locomotive which would combine in a simple and practical manner certain new, with certain old established features of existing practice, so as to vastly increase the power obtainable under present limitations.

The outcome of a determination to meet this *How to* want has resulted in the evolution of the *Obtain it* " GARRATT " locomotive, for which patents have been granted in this and all important countries. This new type which represents an important development in steam locomotive design has been created by reassembling the main components of known conventional types into an arrangement novel in principle and simple in character, giving a combination of many important practical advantages and

How to Obtain it

enabling the locomotive as a whole to be constructed at a less cost than is the case with any other design of locomotive yet produced of a like power.

General Arrangement of " Garratt " Engine

The general arrangement of this new type of engine is that of the duplex bogie, but beyond this it has little in common with other known types. Instead of the boiler being placed above the wheels, as has hitherto been the practice, it is carried upon a girder frame which is pivoted and supported at its extreme ends on bogies each of which may be likened to a locomotive without a boiler. The boiler may lie in the frame as low down as required, whilst these bogies are so constructed that the fuel and water tanks form integral parts of them, thus introducing an entirely new feature. These steam bogies with their water tanks and coal bunker, being the heaviest parts of the engine, are excellently fitted to check any shouldering movement, which is one of

Objections to previous Types of Articulated Locomotives and how removed

the great objections to articulated engines as hitherto built. Indeed so objectionable has this peculiarity been found that in the latest type of such engines various devices are resorted to to check this action, consisting in some cases of side springs and " hangar bolts," all of which are highly undesirable complications, tending to make the movements of the bogies stiff and unnatural and defeating the main object of the bogies by preventing them from accommodating themselves readily to the curvatures of the road. The " GARRATT " engine requires nothing of this sort, and the bogies are free to follow the curvatures and inequalities of the track, which is precisely what a bogie is intended to do, for if the movements of a bogie be checked and hampered by the various spring controls, such as can be seen illustrated in engineering journals of recent date, describing such engines, strains are set up which are detrimental to the engine as a structure, to its ease of running, and to the life of the track it runs over also causing excessive wear of the flanges of the tyres.

In the " GARRATT " engine the tank motor bogies are connected by the rectangular frame which carries the boiler, and as there are no side tanks on this frame, the boiler can be as large as the load gauge will allow, and can be located at any desirable height above the rails, irrespective of the size of the wheels. There is no other type of locomotive in

Special Features of the New Type of Engine

existence which for any given gauge can have so large a boiler and firebox in combination with any required size of driving wheels. Owing to the termination of the carrier frame at the bogie centres, it follows that when the engine is on a curve there are no overhanging ends of either frame or boiler tangential to the curve to impair the stability of the engine as is otherwise found in all other types of articulated locomotives. A consideration of the following diagrams will render this clear.

How Great Steaming Capacity is Obtained The difficulty generally experienced, of obtaining a large grate area of proper proportions is completely removed in the " GARRATT " engine, and was one of the chief reasons which led to the evolution of this type. In these engines of the standard gauge, even under the confined English load gauge, the firebox may be 6ft. 9in. wide inside, and if only seven feet long, and thus practically square, would have a grate area of 47·25 square feet, and this may be increased to over 60 square feet, if required, bearing in mind that there is little question but that two-thirds of the total steam raised in the boiler is generated at, or near the firebox. Thus

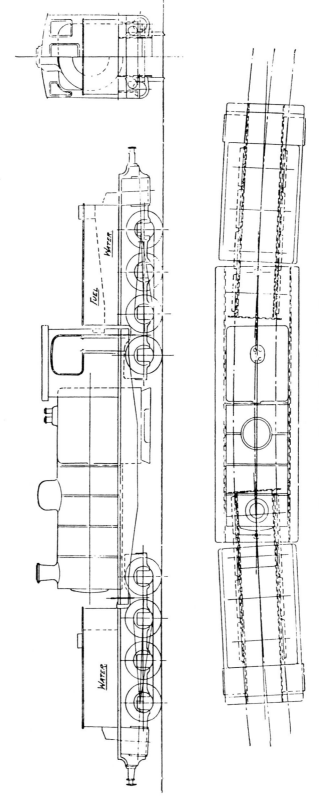

TYPE 0-8-0, 0-8-0
GARRATT

Gauge of Rails 4 feet 8½ inches

Engine on Curve of 330 feet radius

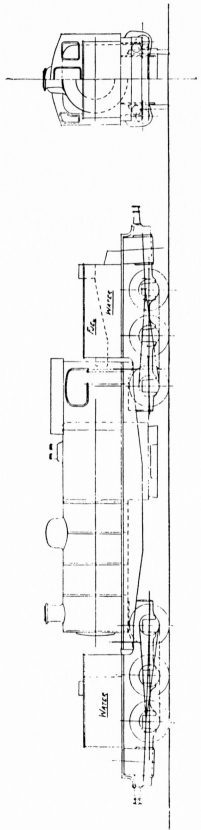

TYPE $\dfrac{\text{0-6-0, 0-6-0}}{\text{GARRATT}}$

Gauge of Rails 5 feet 6 inches

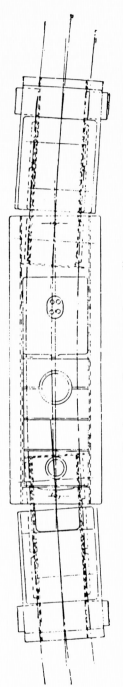

Engine on Curve 330 feet radius

the boiler of the " GARRATT " engine with its large diameter and great number of tubes (which may range up to 600 or more) presents an ideal form for the locomotive. With its large grate area and efficient length of tube, combined with the easy supply of air to the fire, due to the possibility of employing a large rectangular ashpan, the best conditions exist for the proper and economical consumption of fuel and the easy production of ample steam for the heaviest duty.

Among other incidental advantages of the freedom of the boiler from the driving portion of the machine may be mentioned a more efficient and complete clothing of the firebox, and better accessibility for washing out purposes. The locomotive is complete in itself, the tanks on the bogies rendering unnecessary an additional vehicle in the form of a tender.

Some other Features of the 'Garratt' Engine

As the buffing and coupling arrangements are attached to the bogies, they practically adjust themselves to the curves.

The whole arrangement makes for very easy riding, thus conducing to the longevity of the track. The engine forms a perfect double-ender and can be driven in either direction, and if cab first all exhaust steam, smoke, etc., will be left behind, leaving the driver's outlook clear and unobstructed.

Having thus given a general explanation of the leading features of this new type of locomotive, it may be as well for the sake of simplicity and easy reference, to investigate and set forth the details which make up the whole in the form of a catechism, so that any particular point raised may have its answer to hand.

WHAT is a " GARRATT " Locomotive? *Type and* It is an entirely new type of articu- *Capacity* lated locomotive so designed as to give, within the limits of the loading gauge, the greatest possible power for any given weight allowance.

How is such a result obtained? By placing *How* the boiler between two driving systems where *Obtained* the boiler neither interferes with the said driving systems, nor the wheels, nor they with the boiler.

Does this new arrangement entail increased *Simplicity* complication of parts, or greater weight for a given effort? On the contrary the arrangement of the whole engine lends itself to simplicity of design and consequent elimination of useless weight.

How is this desirable end obtained? Because as before mentioned, the boiler and the wheels with their mechanism being independent of each other, ample room is available for increased size and easy grouping of the parts, without having to resort to any crowding or special devices to combine them.

Previous Types

Their Objections and Limits

Are there not other types of Duplex Bogie Locomotives in existence ? Yes, several, but they all suffer from crowding of some of the parts, and from want of a steadying factor for the bogies. The latest form of powerful engine of this type hitherto has a separate tender, which is needless deadweight, entailing a greater first cost, and making the whole machine of great length.   This type has to be turned for every trip, unless run tender first, an objectional and dangerous practice prohibited altogether in many places. Among the disadvantages of this arrangement are the need for very large turntables, 70 or 80, or even 90 feet long, with heavy foundations and a great waste of space for the turntables and the tracks to them.

Unequal Strains in Previous Types

The distribution of weight in the above and other previous types is also a difficulty, and in one case efforts are made to minimize this by transferring part of the weight on the rear wheel system on to the front wheel system by means of a complicated arrangement, necessitating massive castings, bolts, etc., thereby bringing about an uncertain distribution of strains, and tending undoubtedly to render the movements of the bogies when trying to accommodate themselves to the inequalities of the track, restrained and uneasy.

Furthermore, in the type referred to, the *Cramped* firebox has to be placed above the rear system *Fire-boxes* of wheels, thereby rendering it too shallow *and Ash-* and the ashpan very cramped, thus adversely *Pans in* affecting the air supply to the fire and con- *above* sequently the combustion of the fuel and compelling the boiler centre to be unsuitably *High Boilers* high, having regard to the stability of the *in above* engine, especially on rough roads with sharp curves. The disadvantages attached to defective air access to the fire-grate are now receiving considerable attention from railway engineers.

The following remarks from a paper by Mr. *References* Lawford H. Fry, with regard to certain *to previous* actual' tests on the Pennsylvania Railroad, *Difficulties* emphasize this point. (" Combustion and *and* Heat Balances in Locomotives."*) *Impaired* " Evidently the difficulty of getting air to the *Combustion* " fire limited the power of the boiler, and

*Proceedings of Mechanical Engineers, 1908.

" prevented the rate of combustion being
" pushed above 90lbs. of coal per square foot
" per hour."

And again, from the same paper :—

" The figures obtained show that the loco-
" motive series 100 is particularly choked for
" want of air.   The author learned with much
" interest, after writing the foregoing that
" since the tests the Pennsylvania Railroad
" has increased the area of air-inlets in the
" ashpan of this locomotive with the result
" that it steams much more freely and
" efficiently."

And again :—

" At the high rates of combustion the most
" important losses are those due to coal
" escaping unburnt from a lack of sufficient
" air for proper combustion, and hence the
" largest grate by admitting the air most
" freely gives the highest efficiency."

Large Size and Easy Accessibility of Ashpan in 'Garratt' Engine In the " GARRATT " engine the space for the ashpan is not limited in any way, and it is of plain rectangular form and the full width of the grate, thus affording the best possible supply of air. Side doors to the ashpan are provided. Thus the ashes can be cleared out by a man standing at the side of the engine, without the necessity of going underneath. This is a matter of considerable importance in countries where the engine pits are few and far between, and the necessity of keeping the ashpan clear of ashes is worthy of greater attention than it often receives. When the ashes are allowed to accumulate not only is the draught interfered with, but sometimes the firebars are melted and the fire drops down, thus totally disabling the engine. If therefore ready means are provided for cleaning the ashpan the temptation to let the ashes accumulate is removed.

It may be here remarked that, owing to the space available for the firebox in the case of the " GARRATT " engine, which can be not only of large area but deep as well, an excellent wood burning engine can be built on this principle. *Wood Burning 'Garratt' Engines*

The next point that may be dealt with is the disadvantages hitherto experienced by the enforced limitations of the form and capacity of the boiler in ordinary practice.

The Large Boiler of the 'Garratt' Engine

How does the " GARRATT " engine provide a boiler of very great steam producing capacity without any difficulty ? Owing to the absence of side tanks on the central frames which carry the boiler, the whole width of this central

And Large Firebox

portion is available for the boiler and firebox. This width depends on the load gauge of any particular railway, and not on the gauge of the rails. On English railways the width available between the sides of the central portion or frame of the " GARRATT " engine would be about 7 feet 6 inches, so that the outer firebox can be made nearly this width, and the boiler barrel the same. The length of the boiler barrel is entirely optional, but there is no need in this engine to make the barrel and tubes any longer than is required for efficiency. Tubes 10 feet long are ample, and although the extravagantly long boilers of many engines of to-day (which are compulsorily lengthened owing to the arrangement of the wheels) give imposing figures for heating surface, a large percentage is entirely useless for steam raising. In this relation a statement of Mr. S. W. Johnson, late of the Midland Railway, is applicable. When President of the Institution of Mechanical Engineers, 1898, a paper was

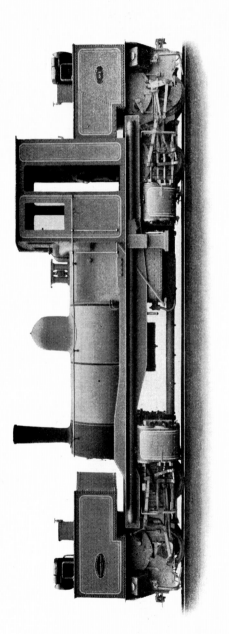
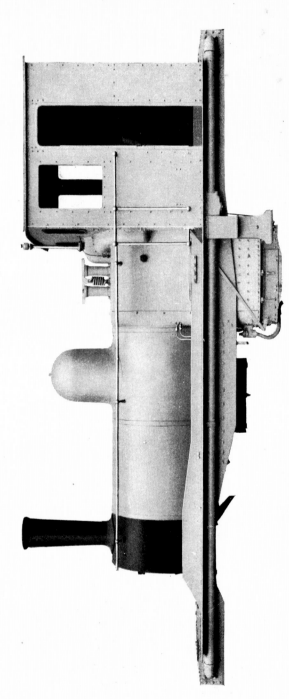

"GARRATT" LOCOMOTIVE for the TASMANIAN GOVERNMENT RAILWAY

2ft. Gauge (North-East Dundas Section)   Full loaded Weight 33½ Tons   The lower Illustration shows the complete Boiler Unit

"GARRATT" LOCOMOTIVE for the DARJEELING-HIMALAYAN RAILWAY

2ft. Gauge   Full loaded Weight 28 Tons   The lower Illustrations show the Locomotive on a reverse curve of 6oft. radius

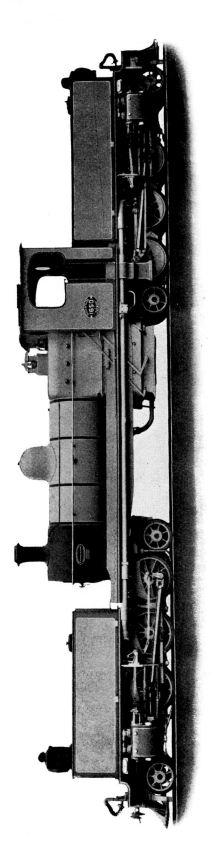

"GARRATT" LOCOMOTIVE for the SOUTH AFRICAN RAILWAYS
3ft. 6in. Gauge   Full loaded Weight $70\frac{1}{2}$ Tons

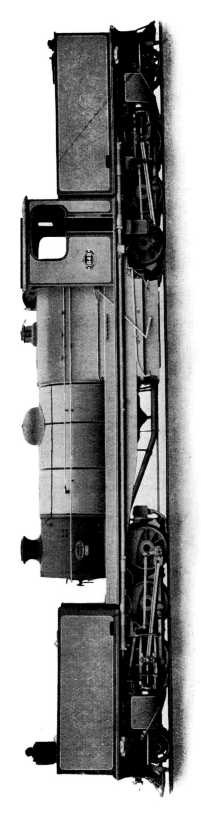

"GARRATT" LOCOMOTIVE for the SOUTH AFRICAN RAILWAYS
3ft. 6in. Gauge   Full loaded Weight $133\frac{3}{4}$ Tons

read entitled " Results of Recent Practical Experience with Express Locomotive Engines," and he, in his remarks on the same, then stated :—

" The tube surface at the smokebox end of
" the boiler had been spoken of by Mr.
" Donkin as much less efficient than at the
" firebox end. There was no doubt that the
" last five or six feet length of the tubes was
" practically of no use for evaporation.
" (Note—the total length of the tubes of his
" single express engines was only 10 feet
" 4 inches). And that the temperature of
" the gases coming into the smokebox was
" rarely much higher than that of the steam.
" The great thing in a locomotive was to get
" as large a firegrate and as big a boiler as
" possible . . . The great question of the day
" with regard to English engines was to
" design an engine that would take a great
" load and at a high speed. This meant a
" big boiler, and perhaps some different form
" of engine from any that was being used now.
" It was a difficult matter now to make an
" express engine of the size it ought to be.
" It had been tried in various ways, and he
" had no doubt the necessity of making some
" change would ultimately bring it about."

Remarks of Mr. S. W. Johnson on Locomotive Boilers

The " Garratt " Steam Locomotive

The Reply of the 'Garratt' Invention to the above

The " GARRATT " engine exactly fulfils Mr. Johnson's prophesied development. There is no doubt that any tube length in excess of ten feet is of little use, and it is obvious that owing to the large diameter of the boiler of the " GARRATT " engines, something like twice the usual number of tubes can be put in, and that the heating

Efficiency of Tube Heating Surface of 'Garratt' Engines

surface in square feet thus utilised has a much greater steam generating capacity than it would have with the same amount of heating surface but with tubes 20 feet long.

Smokebox and Superheater

Are there any difficulties with regard to the space required for the smokebox and parts connected therewith ? None whatever. On the contrary there is ample space for any size or shape of smokebox that may be deemed by locomotive designers to be desirable. This remark applies especially to the use of superheaters, which in some designs need much space, very difficult to provide in engines of the ordinary design.

Ash dropping Arrangement

Can the accumulation of ashes in the smoke-box be well provided for ? Excellently, as owing to the space available, the bottom of the smokebox may be formed as a deep

" hopper," with a valve at the bottom, and thus two advantages are obtained :—

(1). The ashes as they come through the tubes will drop down into the lower portion of this well or pocket out of the way of the draught coming through the tubes, and so will not be liable to be caught up by the blast and thrown out of the chimney, thus avoiding " fire throwing."

(2). As it is not necessary to open the smokebox door to remove ashes, leaky tubes caused by cold air impinging upon them are also prevented. The small valve at the bottom of the hopper can be opened by any suitable lever, and the ashes allowed to flow on to the ground from an outlet only a short distance above it.

Avoidance of Leaky Tubes

Are the weights in the " GARRATT " engine properly distributed over the wheels and rails ? Yes. There is no other existing type of high duty articulated engine in which the weight can be so well distributed. Although the bogies are absolutely independent of each other, the weights on each are practically equal, and their distribution on the

Good Distribution of Weight in 'Garratt' Engines

axles is remarkably even whether the engine be empty or fully loaded with fuel and water. The whole of the weight of the fuel and water goes to increase the adhesion of the wheels on the rails. These desirable features are obtainable to a greater extent in the " GARRATT " engine than in any other design for great power.

Method of Carrying Fuel and Water

How is the necessary fuel and water carried on this engine ? The method of carrying these weights form one of the principal and most interesting features of the " GARRATT" engine, as it is utilized in an ingenious manner for a most important purpose. The tanks and coal bunker are built as integral parts of the bogies, and the result of this—apart from the question of dispensing with a tender, or having to put these tanks and bunkers on the sides of the central frame where they limit the diameter of the boiler—is that their weight, and that of their contents, is utilised not only to increase the adhesion of the wheels, but to serve as a most excellent check to the oscillations of the bogies, thus rendering the running of the engine steady at high as well as at low speeds, and obviating the excessive wear of flanges, hitherto a most

Weight Utilized to assist Traction and to Steady Bogies a Prominent Feature

serious objection to double bogie engines. The great advantage of having these weights directly on the wheels instead of being transmitted to them through the bogie centres hardly requires further emphasis. The capacity of the bunker and tanks is ample and may be made very large indeed, this simply depending on the number of wheels per bogie and the permissible axle loads.

Why does the " GARRATT " principle lend itself to the construction of a very flexible locomotive ? Because for a locomotive to easily negotiate curves and conform to the inequalities of the track the rigid length must be strictly kept within the shortest possible limits, and those engines of exceptional power which have hitherto been constructed, have this objectional rigid length more or less prominent. In the " GARRATT " engine the rigid portion is brought to a minimum, and the whole machine may be said to consist of three lengths articulated, the middle portion being only a little longer than the two end portions. The articulations being quite free it is obvious that the whole conforms with natural freedom

Flexibility on Curves of the Articulated 'Garratt' Engine

to a curve. The accompanying illustrations show this at a glance.

Total Length of 'Garratt' Engine

With regard to the length of such an engine, it must be remembered that it is not one which requires a tender as well, but is a locomotive " proper," that is to say, a loco- motive engine with the necessary supplies for running so many miles, and pulling so much load without further assistance, and therefore the total length is considerably less than it would be if a separate tender was necessary.

Capacity of the 'Garratt' Engine

The power or tractive effort of the " GARRATT " engine depends solely on the permissible load per axle, and the number of coupled axles, because in the case of this type of engine the boiler can be made so large as to be capable of supplying sufficient steam for cylinders of such proportions as may be required to make full use of the adhesive weight.

Let two examples be taken of engines with medium axle loads for the 4ft. 8½in. gauge.

(1). A " GARRATT " engine with 2 sixwheels coupled bogies (0-6-0, 0-6-0 type) with 18 tons per axle. This engine will have a tractive effort of 50,000lbs., equal to pulling at, say, 10 miles per hour 3,000 tons on the level, or 850 tons up 1 in 50 ; the total weight of the engine (no tender) being about 108 tons, and the total length about 62 feet.

(2). A " GARRATT " engine with 2 eight-wheels coupled bogies (0-8-0, 0-8-0 type) with 20 tons load per axle.

This engine will have a tractive effort of 72,000lbs., equal to pulling at, say, 10 miles per hour 4,500 tons on the level or 1,200 tons up 1 in 50 ; the total weight of the engine (no tender) being about 160 tons, and the total length about 67 feet. As showing the possibilities of the " GARRATT " engine in respect of the limitations of usual loco-motive practice, it may be mentioned that in the case of the second example of the " GARRATT " engine quoted above, viz., that with 72,000lbs. tractive force, the longest rigid portion is no greater than about 30 feet.

Why is the " GARRATT " engine superior to others in respect of stability on curves ? It is because the central portion, or more properly, the boiler-carrying frame is pivoted

Superior Stability of 'Garratt' Engines

on to each bogie at each extreme end, and therefore its whole length forms a chord of the curve. Thus, the sharper the curve, the more is the centre of gravity brought inwards.

Steam and Exhaust Pipes

How are the steam and exhaust Pipes arranged ? In the case of a " simple " expansion engine, a single or double regulator as desired, is placed in the dome, and two steam pipes lead from this point, one to the smokebox tubeplate, and one to the firebox end of the boiler, both internally, and from these points suitable connections carry the steam to the cylinders on the bogies. The joints of these steam pipes are located centrally with the turning point of the bogies, only one joint being thus required per bogie. Suitable pipes convey the exhaust steam to the chimney, or, if required, the exhaust from the one system may be passed into the atmosphere direct.

Spacious Cab and Excellent Lookout for Driver

With such a large Boiler as has been referred to, will not the driver's look-out be inconvenient, as even in the large engines of to-day, drivers are practically compelled to lean out of the sides of their cabs in order

" GARRATT " LOCOMOTIVE for the TASMANIAN GOVERNMENT RAILWAY

3ft. 6in. Gauge   Full loaded Weight $94\frac{1}{2}$ Tons

" GARRATT " LOCOMOTIVE for the MOGYANA RAILWAY, BRAZIL

1 metre Gauge   Full loaded Weight $75\frac{3}{4}$ Tons

to keep a look-out for signals ?   On the contrary, the look-out for running in either direction is excellent.   It must be remembered that the boiler has not to be located high up over the wheels as at present, but may be carried low down in the carrier frame, thus allowing plenty of room for the cab windows.   The end illustration shows that in this type of locomotive the provision of a boiler of great size still permits of an outlook as clear and unrestricted as was the case with the early locomotives with their small boilers and low centres of gravity.

Is a convenient " cab " available on this class of engine ? Yes. It may be entirely closed for protection against bad weather, if so desired, or partially open if for warmer climates, and as before stated, the space for look-out windows is all that can be desired. If required, a second cab can be located at *Cab at* the smokebox end, and the engine driven *chimney end* from there, should this be required for any *if desired* special reason.

At first glance the unusual location of the *Weight Dis-* turning centres of the bogies might lead one *tribution on* to conclude that the weights upon the wheels *the Bogies* were unevenly distributed, and that this apparent unequal distribution would be still more accentuated by the variation of load, due to the consumption of coal and water. A little reflection and study of the design will quickly dispel such an impression. The position of these centres, together with the side bearers, is arrived at by accurate calculations of the various weights on the vehicle, and their effect upon the wheels. Obviously the weight of the boiler with its cradle frame is carried by the bogies at such a point as to balance the weights of the cylinders, slide-bars, tanks and contents which lie towards the outer ends of the engine, and to provide the necessary weight on the innermost wheels. With regard to the weight distribution on the wheels being affected by the gradual consumption of the coal and water carried, it must be pointed out that the total weight of the coal and water together bears such a small proportion to the total weight of the bogies, that even if the whole of the water and coal were consumed—which, of course, although possible, is extremely unlikely to be reduced to less than 20%—the variation of the axle loads would be no more, and in many cases less, than is manifest in many tank engines of conventional design and in daily use.

The above information is intended to serve as an introduction of the claims of the " GARRATT " patented type of locomotive to the notice of railway engineers and loco-motive builders.

Specifications, estimates, and all other information, also particulars as to royalties, licences, etc., can be had by applying to Messrs. Beyer, Peacock & Co., Ltd., Gorton Foundry, Manchester, England.

The Origins of the Garratt Locomotive

PART 4

Exploitation of the Patent

Beyer, Peacock must have been granted the sole rights of manufacture in Britain and hence for most new parts of the British Empire. From snippets in later correspondence, it appears that the patent remained the possession of Garratt himself. Presumably Garratt had paid all the fees necessary to secure the patent, and it is probable that he also paid all the initial fees on foreign patents. Later Beyer, Peacock handled payment of renewal fees and subsequently debited his widow. These covered Australia, Belgium, Canada, France, Germany, Italy, Japan and Russia. Garratt seems to have charged £2 per ton on every locomotive constructed. Later the fee became £2 up to 120 tons and thereafter only £1. Out of this Beyer, Peacock took 10% commission, presumably as handling and design charges.

Jackson signed the first Garratt scheme to have cylinders at the outer ends of the engine units which became the standard position on all subsequent designs, This was in February 1908 for the New South Wales Commonwealth Oil Corporation and shows a standard 0-6-0 + 0-6-0. However it was Carl H. Schobelt who prepared the

5) The official builder's photograph of K1, the first Beyer-Garratt Locomotive built, Beyer, Peacock 5292 of 1909.

6a) above and   Two views of K1 in service on the 2ft 0in gauge North East Dundas Tramway in the thick forests where they remained in service until
6b) below   the line closed in 1930. K1 was subsequently shipped back to its builder in 1947 for preservation.

next Garratt scheme which was the one for Tasmania and the original for the K class. Schobelt had been born in Manchester and left Sharp Stewart & Co. in 1888 to work at Beyer, Peacock for the rest of his life. Jackson drew up the next Garratt schemes. There was another for the New South Wales Commonwealth Oil Corporation in April 1908. These would have been large engines, with a length of 61ft, and empty weight 72 tons. This was followed in July by a slightly larger 0-6-0 + 0-6-0 for the 5ft 3ins Central Railway of Brazil when a compound Mallett scheme was offered at the same time. Designs for a Meyer and a Garratt were sent to the Anglo-Chilean Nitrate Railway while the Burma Railways had plans for Fairlies and Mallets to compare with Garratts.

The first two Garratts were shipped from England to Tasmania on 7th October 1909. By the end of that year, over 45 different schemes had been prepared, ranging from four to eight coupled engines and 1ft 6ins to 5ft 6ins gauges. In 1908, a scheme had been prepared for converting Beyer, Peacock's own 1ft 6ins gauge works shunter into a 0-4-0 + 0-4-0 Garratt with cylinders at the inner ends of the bogies, Presumably this was abandoned when the Tasmanian order was received, In April 1909, the Drawing Office was ordered to prepare complete drawings and estimates for a standard gauge 0-6-0 + 0-6-0 for English railways which could be used as a demonstration engine to help convince engineers of the practicability of the type.

In order to help introduce the Garratt more quickly, in November 1909, it was proposed that two or three 0-8-0 + 0-8-0 should be built for the South Manchuria Railway. One was to be sent there free on trial for two or three months "On the understanding that if one fulfils the conditions we claim for it, they place an order with us for two more engines at the same price as the one delivered". These engines would have had 4ft 2ins diam. wheels, 20 x 26ins cylinders, 143.5 tons weight and 63,650lbs. tractive effort. Later a similar proposal was made to the Kalka-Simla Railway for another 0-8-0 + 0-8-0 of even more ambitious design with 4ft wheels, 22 x 26 cylinders, 159 tons weight and 80,220lbs tractive effort. Mr David Patrick, who worked in the Design Office many years later, said that it was probably fortunate that such locomotives were not built then because years of development were needed before engines of such power and size performed really satisfactorily.

Strenuous efforts continued to be made to promote the Garratt, helped no doubt by the successful performance of the first two sent to the North Dundas Tramway in Tasmania. These engines rode well but seem to have been prone to slipping with heavy loads. It was probably lucky that they were compounds because this would have given a more normal exhaust blast up the chimney. All the following Garratts, which were simple, had steaming problems which took some time to resolve. This was true of the 2ft gauge Darjeeling-Himalayan Railway 0-4-0 + 0-4-0 which was ordered in June 1910. It was also prone to slipping on this steeply graded, sharply curved line. One problem may have been the much greater flange friction of the longer trains on the sharp curves, It seems to have been laid aside for a while but eventually was made to perform well on one of the neighbouring lines and was not scrapped until 1954[2].

The next orders were all influenced by the success of the first Tasmanian Garratts. In 1911, the Western Australian Government Railways ordered six 2-6-0 + 0-6-2 to

---

2 For full details of this locomotive see THE NARROW GAUGE No. 79, quarterly journal of the Narrow Gauge Railway Society.

7a) and 7b) The next Garratt locomotive built can be regarded as the true prototype. Works no. 5407 was built in 1910 for the famous 2ft 0in gauge Darjeeling – Himeleye Rly. notorious for its tortuous curves and severe grades. Although it survived until 1954 it was never considered a success and was one of the few Garratt's never to appear in the builder's extensive range of sales literature. *(H. W. Garratt Archive)*

8) Following the success of the pioneer "K" class Tasmania was the destination again for the first main line Garratts. Two "L" class 2-6-2 + 2-6-2 (B.P. 5525-26) and two "M" class 4-4-2 + 4-4-2 Garratts (B.P. 5523-24) were shipped out in 1912. *(H. W. Garratt Archive)*

work over 3ft 6ins. gauge lines with gradients of 1 in 22 and curves 328ft radius. Probably Mr Hume had been to Tasmania and seen the Garratts working there but the steaming problems with the Darjeeling-Himalayan engine must have been the reason why six different types of exhaust-pipe nozzle were tried to see which gave the best results. These were communicated to Beyer, Peacock in September 1912, with the request that the best be fitted to the follow-on order for seven more which were made in 1913. The railway authorities were so well satisfied with this design that, seventeen years later, a further batch of ten was built in their own workshops.

These test results for the exhaust nozzles must have arrived too late to have been incorporated on two designs for the 3ft 6ins gauge sections of the Tasmanian Government Railways. So satisfied was Mr W. R. Deeble with his small Garratts that in 1912 he ordered two "L" class 2-6-2 + 2-6-2 goods type and two 4-4-2 + 2-4-4 "M" class express passenger engines. The "L" class, with 32,050lbs. tractive effort, were 60% more powerful than the largest ordinary type of goods locomotive. The "M" class had 5ft diam. driving wheels powered by four cylinders on each engine unit, the only eight cylinder Garratts ever built. At first, none of these Garratts steamed well, and had to stop every few miles when working up heavy grades in order to get up steam pressure and feed water into the boiler. However, when modified the "M" class proved capable of hauling heavy corridor trains at 55 miles per hour. Garratt's claims about the riding qualities of his design were too amply justified because one of these engines derailed when going round a curve. It was thought that the driver did not realise the high speed of his locomotive because it was travelling so smoothly! In spite of the accident, the performance of these engines did much to establish the Garratt as a highly versatile type of locomotive, suitable for a wide range of duties.

The two 4-6-0 + 0-6-4 sent to the Mogyana Railway in Brazil were greeted with immediate acclaim on their arrival. They were the first metre gauge Garratts and the first of many sent to South America. The steaming problems seem to have been overcome for these engines worked well on their mixed traffic duties and reached

9) and 10)   First of many Garratts sent to South America were the pair of 4-6-0 + 0-6-4 metre gauge locos (b.P. 5529 – 30) for the Mogyana Rly. in Brazil. Three further locos, but with superheated boilers and piston valves, followed in 1914. This particular wheel arrangement was never again used by Beyer, Peacock.

(H. W. Garratt Archive)

11) The first significant order for Garratt locomotives was 6 class Ma (later simply called "M") 3ft 6in gauge 2-6-0 + 0-6-2 locomotives (B.P. 5477-82) for the Western Australian Government Rlys. The original six used saturated steam but when seven more were ordered in 1913 they carried superheaters. With this order the Beyer – Garratt loco had finally "arrived", the last of these pioneers lasting until 1955.   (Beyer – Peacock Ltd.)

speeds of 40 mph on very light track. Three more were supplied in 1914. Another Brazilian Railway, the San Paulo, ordered a solitary 2-6-0 + 0-6-2 for the metre gauge Bragantina branch with sections of 1 in 30 on it. On test, it proved to be more economical than a Beyer, Peacock 4-6-0! An order for a second one did not materialise until 1936, but shows how satisfactory the first must have been.

Garratt's Involvement with the Patent

Just what part Garratt himself played in obtaining these orders we do not know. After his resignation as inspecting engineer for the New South Wales Government Railways in August 1908, he does not seem to have had any other paid employment up to the time of his death. He continued to live in Manchester until 29th September 1911 and had an office at his home in Levenshulme. His printed letter heading used his own painting of a conjectural 0-6-0 + 0-6-0 hauling a rake of open trucks up a 1 in 25 gradient. A visiting card gave his agents as "Beyer, Peacock & Co. Ltd., Manchester; U.S. and Canada, the Baldwin Locomotive Works, Philadelphia. PA.; Germany, Henschel & Sohn, Cassel; Belgium, Soc. St Leonard, Liege". Of these, the only foreign firm to build Garratts during the term of the patent was the Societe St Leonard. Garratt went there in 1912/13 to photograph an 0-6-0 + 0-6-0 for the Congo Railway which had a special experimental type of oil-fired boiler.

Garratt moved to Ellerker Gardens, Richmond, Surrey, to continue promoting his locomotive and other projects. In London, he was in many ways better placed to meet influential people and was involved with the order for a couple of tramway type

TELEGRAMS: "LOCOMOTIVE, RICHMOND—SURREY"

IN YOUR REPLY
PLEASE QUOTE

TO YOUR —

HERBERT W. GARRATT, M.I.MECH.E., F.I.I, ETC.
LOCOMOTIVE ENGINEER.

9 ELLERKER GARDENS,

RICHMOND, SURREY.

191

16. Between 1911 and 1925 the Société Anonyme de Saint-Léonard of Liege in Belgium built a total of 32 750mm gauge 0-6-0 + 0-6-0 Garratts for the Compagnie du Chemins de Fer du Congo. One of the 1919 batch (St Léonard 1901-12, CFC running nos. 112 to 123) is seen here.

(H. W. Garratt Archive)

(Beyer, Peacock Ltd.)

12) A pair of these very attractive 0-6-0 + 0-6-0 Garratts were built for the opening of the Buthidaung-Maungdan 2ft 6in gauge tramway in Burma in 1913 (BP 5702-3). The second smallest Garratt locos built they had an axle loading of only 4 tons. Sadly the tramway closed in 1926 and no further use was found for them.

0-6-0 + 0-6-0 for the 2ft 6ins gauge Buthidaung-Maungdan Tramway in Burma for the Arakan Flotilla Co. In 1913, he met H. Lievsey in London who was partner in the consulting firm which handled much of the South American railway business. He was hoping to receive orders for five from the Buenos Aires & Pacific Railway and possibly two from the Bengal-Nagpur Railway in India. He was confident that the Great Indian Peninsular Railway would place an order for a further couple and discussions were continuing with the South African Railways.

At this period of his life, Garratt was dependent upon the royalties he received from sales of his patent locomotive. He was given advances from Beyer, Peacock which seem to have amounted to £583.66 by the end of July 1913. Garratt wished to receive a further advance of £250 against anticipated orders such as those just mentioned. A projected tour to Brazil had been cancelled, on which Garrett had spent a considerable sum for "outfits", and he considered that some important orders had been missed. He was arranging for publicity in *The Railway News* which would print a special number about his locomotive. He was also working on his ideas for mounting heavy artillery on railway bogies in a way similar to his locomotive. All this was terminated by his death on 25th September 1913. His widow inherited the patent rights.

Beyer, Peacock continue to develop the Garratt

It might well have been thought that, on Garratt's death, Beyer, Peacock would have lost interest in promoting his design but, on the contrary, they continued to place great hopes in it and eventually this form of articulated locomotive became the main-stay of their production at Gorton. In 1915, three special 2-4-0 + 0-4-2 were delivered to work on the 5ft 3ins section of the Sao Paulo Railway between Santos and Piassaguera. Although perfectly level, there were some light-built bridges here. The Garratts were introduced to haul heavier trains because their wheel-base of 47ft 10ins spread their

13) In 1913 Brazil's Sao Paulo Rly. ordered this 2-6-0 + 0-6-2 Beyer-Garratt for their metre gauge Bragantine branch (B.P. 5664). A second similar loco followed in 1936 (B.P. 6795).

(Beyer, Peacock Ltd.)

14) Beyer – Garratt locos are more associated with Southern Africa then anywhere else in the world so the first ones to be delivered there are of particular interest. They were three Class NG G11 2-6-0 + 0-6-2 locos for South Africa's 2ft gauge lines, B.P. 5975-77. It is worthy of note that the last Beyer Garratt locos built, by Hunslet in 1967-8, were also for these railways.

(Beyer, Peacock Ltd.)

weight over a long length. They performed their duties very satisfactorily until replaced by diesels in 1950.

The First World War stopped further development on the Garratt and in particular on three designs for the South African Railways. One design was for three 2-6-0 + 0-6-2 for their 2ft gauge lines which were delivered in 1919. These were the first of many for this gauge, ending, as far as Beyer, Peacock was concerned, with the last steam locomotive built at Gorton in 1958, the type having been improved into a 2-6-2 + 2-6-2. Three have been brought back to operate on the Welsh Highland Railway in North Wales. The necessity for the inner carrying wheels was shown by trials on the 3ft 6ins "GB" class, delivered to South Africa in 1920. Beyer, Peacock's engine erector, W. Wakefield, had a cradle slug beneath the boiler barrel in order to watch the action of the wheels. From this he was able to point out the importance of the inner carrying wheels in guiding the engine units round curves.

But, in some ways, the heavier "GA" class Garratt was the more important even though only one of its type was built. It was designed to rival the North British "MH" class Mallet. The Garratt weighed 133.8 tons in working order and produced 53,700 lb tractive effort. The Mallet, weighing 179 tons, was rated at 48,370lb tractive effort. On test up the Waschbank-Wessels Nek section with gradients of 1 in 75, the Garratt hauled 1,451 tons in $26^1/_2$ minutes compared with the Mallet's 1,303 tons in $32^1/_2$ minutes. The Garratt's coal consumption was 14.18lbs per 100 ton-miles, as against 16.57lbs for the Mallet. The South African Railways were so convinced by the superiority of the Garratt that, although they already had 79 Mallets, they never ordered any more.

Through the First World War when no locomotives could be built, the patent was extended to June 1928. Mrs Garratt was an executrix of her husband's will and the income from the patent must have been left to her and their daughter. At the time of Garratt's death, £864.18.9 had been paid to him, possibly some of this as advances, and he was probably in debt to Beyer, Peacock. During the War, Beyer, Peacock must have lent a considerable amount to Mrs Garratt to help her bring up her daughter because she seems to have had no other income. A sum paid quarterly must have been agreed. At one time this was not received and Mrs Garratt feared that she might lose her home if she could not meet debts owed elsewhere.

The first definite figures that survived show her owing £2,696.6.4 in 1922 when some of her debt may have been repaid. By that time, more orders were being received, boosted by the success if the South African and other engines. Sufficient royalties had been received for this debt to be settled in 1923 and in addition she was paid £50 in 1923 and £87.14.4 in 1924. Records show that she received £3,151 in 1925, £2,314 in 1926 but this may have been only for 6 months, £5,951 in 1927 and £3,825 up to June 1928 when the patent expired. These last sums seem to have incurred a higher rate of Income Tax, much to Mrs Garratt's annoyance. Beyer, Peacock would not countenance any extension of payments beyond the expiry of the patent because competition was so severe.

H. W. Garratt never lived to see the full development of his type of locomotive. Later Beyer, Peacock would build examples that worked on the world's highest railways in the Andes, as well as the largest steam locomotive in Europe, that sent to Russia in

1932; the most powerful steam locomotives in Australia, those for New South Wales in 1952; the biggest steam locomotives for the metre gauge, the East African Railways 59 class in 1955. Such locomotives fully justified the claim made in 1912,

> "Our experience in the trade leads us to believe with great confidence that the "Garratt" has come to stay, and that it is destined to supersede most existing types of articulated engines, and, indeed, to extend the use of that particular type of locomotive altogether".

Background to the Brochure

We have seen how H. W. Garratt's patent for a new type of articulated locomotive was granted in June 1908 and then in September how he signed a formal agreement with Beyer, Peacock which settled the terms of royalties, licences, etc. and made this company his agents in Britain. Garratt established an office at Levenshulme in Manchester and had special note paper printed. Staff in the Beyer, Peacock's Drawing Office helped prepare schemes so together they continued to develop and exploit the patent. A four page brochure was printed to explain the features of this new design and various railway companies were approached.

Garratt's claims for his locomotive were seen to be justified though practical experience gained with the first two designs, the pair of K class compounds for the Tasmanian Government's North Dundas Tramway sent in October 1909 as well as the one for the Darjeeling-Himalayan Railway ordered in June 1910. Beyer, Peacock were obviously impressed with the potential of Garratt's concept because, at their Annual General Meeting in March 1911, their Chairman said that he believed the Garratt design was

> "destined to have a good future, and, as we hope, to replace all other existing types of articulated locomotives whenever it may meet them in open competition. It requires not test of time and experience owing to a new principle being involved, but rather constitutes a new application of sound proved and well-tried mechanical principles and it is this fact which is at the base of our confidence in its success... Probably few innovations in locomotive practice have met with so speedy recognition and appreciation". (Beyer, Peacock Co. Ltd. Minutes, No. 1, 1st March 1911).

Accordingly it was decided to produce more extensive publicity in the form of a bigger brochure which was issued in 1911 and formed the basis of this reprint.

The brochure outlines the new features Garratt introduced, with particular emphasis on the potential for a well-designed boiler. We can imagine him reflecting on his struggles to maintain steam on narrow-gauge locomotives with fireboxes restricted by the driving wheels, or, with boilers placed high above the wheels, problems of seeing the track ahead. Garratt's boilers could be designed with large fireboxes, large diameter barrels with more shorter tubes to give free steaming. Weight distribution is also discussed, with claims that, having the fuel and water supplies on the bogies, greater stability was achieved, less strain on the pivots and more even weight on the wheels.

Some of these points obviously needed illustrating, as well as the need to show that his locomotive was not just a small narrow-gauge type but was equally suited for the most powerful locomotives. One drawing submitted for the patent shows a 2-4-0 + 0-4-2 with large driving wheels but those included in the brochure are more typical of the usual concept of the Garratt at this time. They have been taken from schemes prepared for various companies and show large, powerful locomotive, with only driving wheels. It may have been the performance of the first two types of Garratt actually built which pointed to the need for bogies or other carrying wheels to guide the locomotives

15) Herbert Garratt's painting of an imaginary 0-6-0 + 0-6-0 Garratt hard at work on a steep grade.

(H. W. Garratt Archive)

round curves. The first two designs, the 0-6-0 + 0-6-0, 2ft 6ins gauge for the Arakan Flotilla Company, Burma, and the four 0-4-0 + 0-4-0 standard gauge industrial locomotives were the only ones built by Beyer, Peacock without extra carrying wheels.

Garratt fancied himself as an artist and painted two oil pictures to help publicise his invention. Both are in monochrome so presumably must have been intended to be used for preparing printing blocks. The first shows an imaginary 0-6-0 + 0-6-0 hauling a goods train up an incline of 1 in 25. He could not have been satisfied with the perspective because he had the canvas mounted cock-eyed behind the framing to increase the impression of a steep gradient. He used this picture as the frontispiece and the other at the back of the brochure. In the second, he was demonstrating how, in his design of locomotive, the boiler could be suspended low down in its cradle so that the cab could be fitted with big windows to give an improved view of the track ahead. It should be noted how most of the large signal gantry is clearly visible. In the earliest sketches of his new locomotives, Garratt drew a cab at both ends of the boiler frame, a feature also mentioned in the brochure which would have given an even better view when running chimney first but something never attempted by Beyer, Peacock.

Garratt's widow inherited his patent rights. After the First World War, both she and Beyer, Peacock must have wanted to stimulate interest in and orders for the Garratt locomotive as they realised this would help boost sales. Accordingly the 1911 brochure was re-issued. While the text remained the same, additional photographs were included, resulting in the copy which has been reprinted. It will be seen that the photographs cover the first two types already mentioned orders for the Tasmanian Government 4-4-2 + 2-4-4 express type of 1912 and the Mogyana Railway, Brazil, 4-6-0 + 0-6-4 passenger type. Then there are the two 3ft 6ins types for the South African Railways, the heavy GA class of which there was only the one and the lighter GB of which six more were built later. These photos must place this edition of the brochure around 1912. By that time, Beyer, Peacock had manufactured eleven different designs for seven different companies. The Tasmanian Government had ordered three different types. The Western Australian Government Railways and the Mogyana Railway had placed repeat orders while the San Paulo Railway had also ordered two different types. But it was really the South African Railways three which helped to establish the Garratt as the most successful type of fully articulated steam locomotive. This was remarkable progress in quite a short time for a new type of specialised locomotive.

Orders for Garratt Locomotives up to 1922

Built by Beyer, Peacock

Order No.	No. Built	Wheel Arrangement	Date	Gauge	Name of Railway
9954	2	0-4-0 + 0-4-0	1909	2.0	Tasmanian Government
094	1	0-4-0 + 0-4-0	1910	2.0	Darjeeling-Himalayan, India
0246	6	2-6-0 + 0-6-2	1911	3.6	Western Australian Government
0303	2	4-4-2 + 2-4-4	1912	3.6	Tasmanian Government
0304	2	2-6-2 + 2-6-2	1912	3.6	Tasmanian Government
0322	2	4-6-0 + 0-6-4	1912	metre	Mogyana, Brazil
0537	1	2-6-0 + 0-6-2	1912	metre	Sao Paulo, Brazil
0557	7	2-6-0 + 0-6-2	1913	3.6	Western Australian Government
0588	2	0-6-0 + 0-6-0	1913	2.6	Arakan Flotilla, Burma
0695	3	4-6-0 + 0-6-4	1914	metre	Mogyana, Brazil
0810	3	2-4-0 + 0-4-2	1915	5.6	Sao Paulo, Brazil
0941	1	2-6-0 + 0-6-2	1920	3.6	South African, GA class
0942	1	2-6-2 + 2-6-2	1920	3.6	South African, GB class
01060	3	2-6-0 + 0-6-2	1919	2.0	South African, NG/G11

Built by the Societe Anonyme St Leonard, Belgium

Order No.	No. Built	Wheel Arrangement	Date	Gauge	Name of Railway
	1	0-4-0 + 0-4-0	1911	600mm	Vicinaux du Mayumbe, Belgium Congo
	1	0-6-0 + 0-6-0	1911	750mm	Chemin de Fer du Congo
	1	0-4-0 + 0-4-0	1912	750mm	Zaccar Mines, North Africa
	12	0-6-0 + 0-6-0	1919	750mm	Chemin de Fer du Congo

17) Many UK readers will have become familiar with the later 2ft Gauge South African Garratt locos that have been brought into Britain in recent years. Typical of such imports is NGG 16 class Garratt 119 (Beyer, Peacock 6926/1937) seen at Umzinto, Natal in the 1950's.

(the late Anthony Spit)